the big house

this is a big house

can you see the big green tree

---

first draw the house

next colour it in

**now write this out and write
in the words**

this is the big _ _ _ _ _

there is a green _ _ _ _ next to it

3

this is the back of the big house

can you see some things to sleep on

can you see a big orange and
blue umbrella

---

draw the umbrella

now colour it orange and blue

this is the garden next to the house

the garden is green

there is a playhouse in the garden

can you see an apple tree

there are some red and green apples
on the tree

---

draw and colour the apple tree

write
this is an _ _ _ _ _ tree

these playthings are in the garden

it is good fun to go on them and
to play with them

---

draw the playthings

write

there are some things to play on
in the _ _ _ _ _ _

at the end of the garden there
is a garden dump

can you see these things on the
garden dump

    some apples
    a brown box
    an egg with a crack
    some ink
    a letter
    a rock
    a black spring
    a red ribbon
    a yellow van with a bump in it
    a tin can

**draw some of the things from
the dump**

12

next to the dump there is a big tree

there are some things under the tree

and there are some things up in
the tree

can you see them

**draw the tree and the things in
it and under it**

write
this tree is at the end of the
_ _ _ _ _ _

there is a house up in the tree

it is a tree house

can you see the yellow letter box

there are some words on it

they are in orange letters

can you read them

eggin greenback

---

draw a big letter box

colour it yellow

write the words on it

eggin greenback lives in the tree

he goes to sleep in the tree house

he is in the tree now

he is next to the tree house

---

write this out

eggin greenback lives in the tree

he can go to sleep in the
tree _ _ _ _ _

now eggin greenback is coming
down from the tree

he is coming down to the garden

jump

eggin drops down

---

write these words out

eggin _____ comes down
from the tree

this is eggin greenback

his back is green

---

draw eggin greenback

write

this is eggin greenback

his back is _ _ _ _ _

eggin is happy to see his playthings

he picks some up

he puts some down

he jumps onto a rock

---

draw eggin up on the rock

write this
eggin is _ _ _ _ _ to see his playthings

eggin gets back into his tree

he goes into his tree house

he is going to stop there and
get some sleep

can you see eggin jumping up onto
his mattress